THE SCRIBNER
RADIO MUSIC LIBRARY

Edited by
ALBERT E. WIER

VOLUME II
MODERN COMPOSITIONS
. . .
PIANO

NEW YORK
CHARLES SCRIBNER'S SONS

THE SCRIBNER RADIO MUSIC LIBRARY

VOLUME II—COMPOSITIONS BY MODERN COMPOSERS

TABLE OF CONTENTS—TITLES

THE SCRIBNER RADIO MUSIC LIBRARY

VOLUME II—COMPOSITIONS BY MODERN COMPOSERS

TABLE OF CONTENTS—COMPOSERS

A Guide Through Volume II

THE volumes of the SCRIBNER RADIO MUSIC LIBRARY are devoted entirely to compositions which are heard constantly over the great broadcasting chains—played by orchestras, chamber music organizations, or instrumental soloists; sung by choral organizations or by vocal soloists. Each of the nine volumes contains only the choicest and most popular of its particular type of music.

This volume contains the works of modern composers, many of them contemporary, ranging from Grieg to Tschaikowsky, and opens with the spirited **Hungarian Dance, No. 5,** by Johannes Brahms. One of Brahms' greatest accomplishments was his setting of Hungarian folk melodies in sixteen separate dances,

BRAHMS and they are played in orchestral form as well as for both piano and violin solo. Another of this master's beautiful compositions is the **Intermezzo, Op. 117, No. 1,** the theme of which is an exquisite cradle song, quite as beautiful as his other famous lullaby. Brahms is also represented by four waltzes selected from the **Waltzes, Op. 39,** one of which, the one in A♭ Major, has been the means of making the name of Brahms beloved of the entire world.

DVOŘÁK Four widely broadcast compositions by Antonin Dvořák follow, all of which are favorites. One is the world-famous **Humoreske, Op. 101, No. 7,** which is played and sung in every conceivable manner; another, the **Largo from the New World Symphony,** a greatly admired orchestral number, the melody of which has been popularized enormously as a kind of synthetic negro spiritual under the title, "Going Home." Many orchestras and violinists play the **Slavonic Dance, No. 1,** to the enjoyment of millions, and the fairylike **Waltzes, Op. 54, No. 1,** are also heard repeatedly.

SOME MIS- Claude Debussy may be classed among the not too numerous French composers whose works **CELLANEOUS** will endure, and his **Rêverie** gives ample proof of the genius which later created the wonder-**COMPOSERS** ful symphonic poem, "The Afternoon of a Faun." Gabriel Fauré, another Frenchman whose symphonic, choral, and chamber music works have brought him fame, contributes an exquisite **Romance Sans Paroles,** and the brilliant Spaniard, Enrique Granados, whose successful career was cut short when he was drowned while on an English vessel during the Great War, composed many brilliant Spanish dances of which the **Playera, Op. 5,** presented herewith, is a great radio favorite.

GRIEG No composer who ever lived possessed the gift of melodic invention to a higher degree than Edvard Grieg—his music may be said to sing its way into the hearts of the radio audience. He is amply represented in this volume by the exquisite **To Spring, Op. 43, No. 6,** two excerpts from his colorful incidental music to "Peer Gynt," titled **Anitra's Dance** and **Ase's Death**; the intense delight he always experienced at native village festivals is reflected in the **Norwegian Dances, Op. 35, Nos. 1 and 2,** and his remarkable ability to paint pictures in music is amply evidenced in the **Erotik, Op. 43, No. 5; Puck, Op. 71, No. 3;** and **Spring Dance, Op. 38, No. 5.**

MORE MIS- As the pages of this volume unfold, a number of frequently broadcast compositions reveal **CELLANEOUS** themselves. There is exquisite charm in the **Cradle Song** by the Russian, Ilyinsky; calm **COMPOSERS** and contentment in Adolf Jensen's **Murmuring Zephyr;** the fire of Scandinavia in Per Lasson's **Crescendo;** the perfume of flowers in the **Butterfly** by the Canadian composer, Calixa Lavallée; the whimsical side of the Russian in Levine's **Humoreske;** memories of Marie Antoinette in Liadow's **Musical Snuff-Box.**

MacDOWELL Our own American composer, Edward MacDowell, has many works which are popular with the radio audience. Pianists frequently play his **Witches' Dance, Op. 17, No. 2,** the melodic line of which resembles an arrow in its flight; another great favorite is the **Scotch Poem, Op. 31, No. 2,** which reflects not alone the bonny banks but the fearsome crags as well of Scotland; and in gentler harmonic, as well as melodic mood, is the beautiful **Idyl, Op. 28, No. 1.**

MOSZ-KOWSKI It would be hard to determine whether Moritz Moszkowski's **Spanish Dances, Op. 12, Nos. 1 and 2,** or his **Serenata, Op. 15,** are heard more frequently over the radio, but they are all quite deservedly favorite numbers. Moszkowski was not only a fine composer, but a man of letters and a thorough sportsman—one of his penchants was billiards, at which he was a master. The smooth clarity of his musical thought is evidenced also in the suave **Mélodie, Op. 18, No. 1.**

MORE MIS-CELLANEOUS COMPOSERS In these days when broadcasting has made good music so much more appreciated, we hear many compositions played that otherwise might never be heard, such as the **Serenade** by the Swedish composer, Ole Olsen; then there is **May Night** by the Finnish master, Selim Palmgren, with its oddly opaque harmonies; we are reminded of the creative genius of the pianist Paderewski in compositions such as the famous **Minuet** and the **Mélodie, Op. 8, No. 3,** also titled "Chant du Voyageur." Another number that delights with its lilting gayety is the **Serenade** by the Frenchman, Gabriel Pierné.

RACH-MANINOFF It is said that Sergei Rachmaninoff, mighty pianist and mightier composer, has often expressed his regret that his fame in the latter capacity revolves so closely around the universally popular **Prelude in C♯ Minor, Op. 3, No. 2,** and we are inclined to agree with him because his **Prelude in G Minor, Op. 23, No. 5,** is equally impressive. Other of his compositions in this volume which are broadcast include the picturesque **Polichinelle, Op. 3, No. 4,** and the marvellously expressive but all too brief **Romance.**

MORE MIS-CELLANEOUS COMPOSERS With the wonderful pages of the above-mentioned works behind us, we are plunged into a veritable maze of striking works by modern composers. There is the soulful **Cavatina, Op. 85, No. 3,** by Joachim Raff, the **Romance, Op. 15, No. 2,** of Nicholas Rimsky-Korsakow, with its suggestion of odd rhythm. The French composer, Camille Saint-Saëns, is adequately represented by the **Minuet, Op. 56,** and also by that haunting melody, originally written for the 'cello, and so exquisitely danced to by Pavlowa, **The Swan.** Philipp Scharwenka, distinguished composer and brother of the famous pianist, Xaver Scharwenka, contributes the picturesque **Gondellied, Op. 63, No. 3.** Edward Schütt, an adept in the composition of salon piano music, presents the favorite **A la Bien Aimée.** Jean Sibelius, the Finnish composer, whose symphonic tone-poem, "Finlandia," won him international renown, fascinates us with that weird dance of death, **Valse Triste,** and his deeply emotional **Romance, Op. 24, No. 9.** Christian Sinding depicts with a master's hand the approach of the vernal season in his **Rustle of Spring;** Richard Strauss reveals a rare vein of poetic fancy in the **Träumerei, Op. 9, No. 4,** while we often hear pianists play the **Berceuse, Op. 3, No. 2,** by Alexander Spendiarow, and the haunting **Elégie, Op. 1, No. 3,** by Sergei Youféroff, both Russians of remarkable ability.

TSCHAI-KOWSKY There is little doubt that the works of Peter Tschaikowsky rank with those of Rimsky-Korsakow in radio popularity. The **Andante from the Fifth Symphony** and the **Andante Cantabile** from his string quartets, Op. 11, are frequently heard and are included in this volume with a transcription for piano of the delightful **Mélodie, Op. 42, No. 3,** for violin. You will also find the **Chant Sans Paroles, Op. 2, No. 3,** the **Barcarolle, Op. 37, No. 6,** which is an ode in praise of June; the **Romance, Op. 5,** the tiny mosaic from the Children's Album, **Valse, Op. 39, No. 8,** and the fantastically spirited **Humoreske, Op. 10, No. 2.** There are other works of Tschaikowsky, from his grand operas and ballets, in Volume IV and Volume V.

Hungarian Dance No. 5

JOH. BRAHMS

Waltzes
(Selected)

Tempo giusto

JOH. BRAHMS, Op. 39

14

Intermezzo

JOH. BRAHMS, Op. 117, No. 1

Più Adagio

pp sempre ma molto espressivo

Un poco più Andante

Slavonic Dance

Presto

ANTON DVOŘÁK, Op.46, No.1

CODA

Humoreske

ANTON DVOŘÁK Op. 101, № 7

Poco lento e grazioso

Più lento

Waltzes

ANTON DVOŘÁK, Op.54, № 1

Largo
(New World Symphony)

ANTON DVORÁK

Tempo I

Rêverie

CLAUDE DEBUSSY

Romance Sans Paroles

G. FAURÈ, Op. 17, No. 3

Playera
Spanish Dance

E. GRANADOS, Op. 5, No. 5

Andantino, quasi Allegretto

con Pedale sempre ad lib.

Anitra's Dance
(Peer Gynt)

EDVARD GRIEG

Tempo di Mazurka

To Spring
(An Den Frühling)

EDVARD GRIEG, Op. 43, № 6

Allegro appassionato

Erotik

EDVARD GRIEG. Op. 43, Nº 5.

Norwegian Dance

Allegretto tranquillo e grazioso

ED. GRIEG, Op. 35, № 2

Norwegian Dance

ED. GRIEG, Op. 35, No. 3

Allegro moderato alla marcia

il Basso marcato

Puck

KOBOLD

ED. GRIEG, Op. 71, No 3

Ase's Death
(Peer Gynt)

EDVARD GRIEG

Spring Dance

EDVARD GRIEG

Lullaby
(from "Noure and Anitra" Suite)

A. ILYINSKY, Op. 13

Murmuring Zephyrs

ADOLF JENSEN

Murmurando, con delicatezza

Crescendo

PER LASSON

78

Le Papillon
(The Butterfly)

CALIXA LAVALLÉE

Humoreske

M. LEVINE, Op. 6

A Music Box
(Une Tabatière à Musique)
Valse - Badinage

A. LIADOW, Op. 32

sempre staccato

Witches' Dance
(Hexentanz)
Op.17, Nº 2.

EDWARD MAC DOWELL

Presto. (♩.=126)

Idyl

EDWARD MACDOWELL, Op. 28, No. 1

Scotch Poem

E. MACDOWELL, Op. 31, No. 2

Spanish Dance

M. MOSZKOWSKI, Op. 12, No. 1

Mélodie

M. MOSZKOWSKI Op. 18, No. 1

Serenata

M. MOSZKOWSKI, Op. 15, No. 1

Spanish Dance

M. MOSZKOWSKI, Op. 12, No. 2

Gopak

M. MOUSSORGSKY

Allegro vivace

Serenade

OLE OLSEN

Menuet à l'antique

IGNACE J. PADEREWSKI

Allegretto

Brillante

CODA
Vivo

Mélodie

I. J. PADEREWSKI, Op. 8, No 3

Andante grazioso e moderato

May Night

SELIM PALMGREN

Sérénade

GABRIEL PIERNÉ

Prèlude

S. RACHMANINOFF Op. 3, No. 2

poco   et   poco   cresc.

Tempo I.

Prélude

S. RACHMANINOFF, Op. 23, No. 5

Alla marcia

Un poco meno mosso

poco a poco accelerando e cresc. al *Tempo Primo*

Tempo Primo

Polichinelle

S. RACHMANINOFF, Op. 3, No. 4

Romance

S. RACHMANINOFF

Andantino, quasi sognando

Cavatina

JOACHIM RAFF

Larghetto quasi andantino

Romance

N. RIMSKY - KORSAKOW, Op 15, No. 2

Andantino espressivo

Le Cygne
(The Swan)

C. SAINT-SAËNS

Adagio et legato

Minuet

C. SAINT-SAËNS, Op. 56

Gondellied

PHILIPP SCHARWENKA Op. 63, No. 3

A la bien-aimée

Valse

ED. SCHÜTT, Op. 59, Nº 2

Tempo di Valse moderato e cantabile

Molto meno, mosso tranquillo

amoroso e molto espressivo

poco rit.

Romance

JEAN SIBELIUS, Op. 24, № 9

Valse triste
(From the drama "Kuolema")

JEAN SIBELIUS, Op. 44

Rustle of Spring

Frühlingsrauschen

CHR. SINDING, Op. 32, No. 3

Agitato

Con Pedale sempre

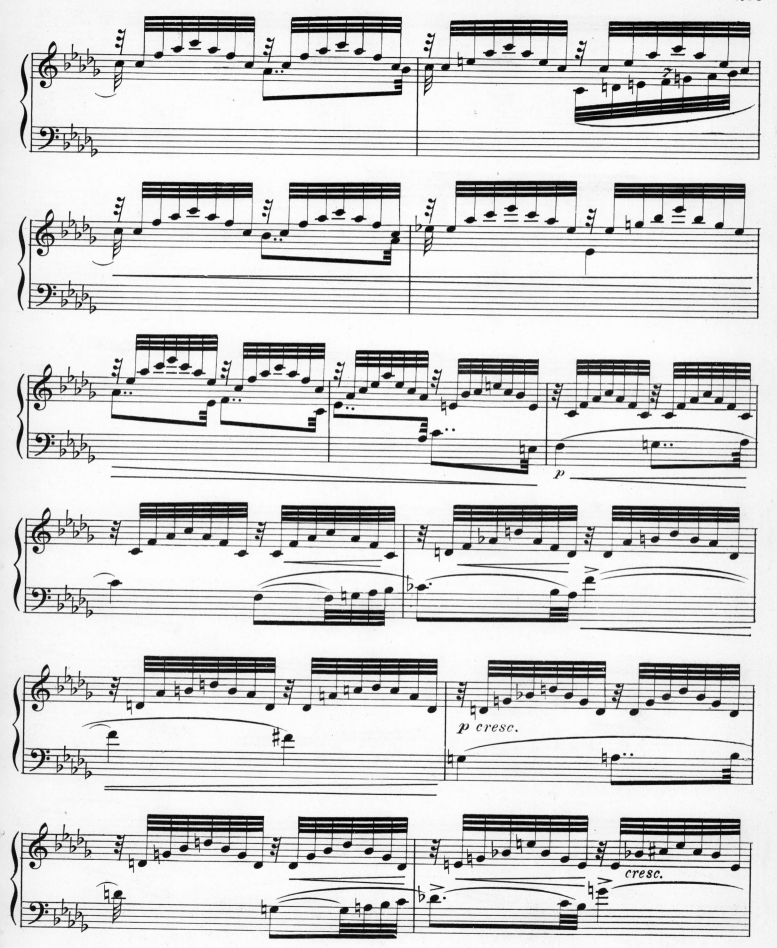

Berceuse

Andante cantabile

A. SPENDIAROW Op.3 No.2

Traümerei

RICHARD STRAUSS, Op. 9, Nº 4

Andante Cantabile
(Fifth Symphony)

P. TSCHAIKOWSKY, Op. 64

Andante cantabile
(Quartet Op. 11)

P. TSCHAIKOWSKY

Andante cantabile

La melodia molto espressiva ed un poco marcato, l'accompagnamento sempre **ppp**

Chant sans Paroles

P. TSCHAIKOWSKY

Allegretto grazioso e cantabile

Romance

P. TSCHAIKOWSKY. Op. 5

"June" Barcarolle

P. TSCHAIKOWSKY, Op. 37, No 6

Poco più mosso

Tempo I

Mélodie

P. TSCHAIKOWSKY, Op. 42, No. 3

Andante con moto

Humoresque

P. TSCHAIKOWSKY, Op. 10, No. 2

Allegretto scherzando

Semplice, ma espress.

Valse
(Children's Album)

P. TSCHAIKOWSKY, Op. 39, No. 8

Élégie

S. YOUFERÓFF, Op. 1, Nº 3

Tempo I
mf
rubato
rit.
piu mosso
pp
meno mosso
leggiero
rall.
ppp
ten